THE TURING TESTS

EXPERT
CODE
BREAKERS

Foreword by Sir Dermot Turing

ARCTURUS

ARCTURUS

This edition published in 2019 by Arcturus Publishing Limited
26/27 Bickels Yard, 151–153 Bermondsey Street,
London SE1 3HA

ISBN: 978-1-78888-751-9
AD006770NT

Printed in the UK

CONTENTS

FOREWORD

Alan Turing's last published paper was about puzzles. It was written for the popular science magazine *Penguin Science News*, and its theme is to explain to the general reader that while many mathematical problems will be solvable, it is not possible ahead of time to know whether any particular problem will be solvable or not.

Alan Turing's work at Bletchley Park is well known: unravelling one of the most strategically important puzzles of World War II, the Enigma cipher machine. The Enigma machine used a different cipher for every letter in a message; the only way to decipher a message was to know how the machine had been set up at the start of encryption, and then to follow the mechanical process of the machine. The codebreakers had to find this out, and the answer was not in the back of the book. To begin with, they had squared paper and pencils, and they had to work out the cipher-machine's daily settings, using intuition and ingenuity. These characteristics constitute mathematical reasoning, according to Alan Turing, who was confident that there was no difference between the reasoning processes of a human provided with pencil, paper and rubber, and those of a computer.

Although they did not have computers to help them at Bletchley Park, with Alan Turing's help new electrical and electronic devices were invented which sifted out impossible and unlikely combinations and so reduced the puzzle to a manageable size. And the experience with these new machines laid the foundation for the development of electronic digital computers in the post-war years.

Computers are now commonplace, not only in the workplace and on a desk at home, in a smartphone or tablet, but in almost every piece of modern machinery. Teaching people computer skills and coding are now considered obvious elements of the curriculum. Except that this is not so, in all parts of the world. In Africa, access to computers in schools is extremely variable, and in some countries there is little or no opportunity for students to have hands-on experience of a real computer. For example, in Malawi, students may have only an 8 per cent chance of using a computer at home, whereas once their school is equipped with computers over 90 per cent of students can get access to what most of us consider to be essential technology. Providing computers motivates

students, with 98 per cent saying that learning is more enjoyable when they have the use of a computer.

The Turing Trust, a charity founded by Alan Turing's great-nephew James in 2009, aims to confront these challenges in a practical way which honours Alan Turing's legacy in computer development. The Turing Trust provides still-working used computers to African schools, enabling computer labs to be built in rural areas where students would otherwise be taught about computers with blackboard and chalk. The computers are refurbished and provided with an e-library of resources relevant to the local curriculum, and then sent out to give a new purpose and bring opportunity to underprivileged communities.

Thank you for buying this book and supporting the Turing Trust.

Sir Dermot Turing
October 2018

To find out more, visit www.turingtrust.co.uk

Notes to the reader
The puzzles in this book are not intended for the faint-hearted, but are designed to challenge experienced puzzle solvers. They are graded in three levels of difficulty, with the puzzles in the third level being truly for experts.

Unless otherwise stated the quotes in the book are by Alan Turing.

HIDDEN WORDS

Can you find the names of five well-known **British novelists** which have been concealed within the sentences below?

My beau stencilled a floral design.

I bought wool, forgetting that my needles were broken.

We washed our hands for sterilization.

Tomorrow, linguists will lecture us about speech development.

I observed the beautiful shell, eyes wide with admiration.

LOGIC PUZZLE

Read the following text and see if you can answer the final question.

There are roadworks taking place on three roads: Lombard Road, Merton Road and New Park Road. One is for electricity works, one for gas works and one for water works. One is scheduled to take a week, one two weeks and one a month. The following is also true:

- Merton Road's works are going to take longer than the electricity works.

- The works that are going to take two weeks are on a road that is later in the alphabet than the road on which gas works are taking place.

- Lombard road is not having gas works.

- The electricity works will take longer than the water works.

Based on this information, can you deduce which works are happening on which road, and for how long?

ANAGRAM + 1

Each of the following lines contains a scrambled word plus one extra letter. These extra letters, when read from top to bottom, will reveal a topic which fits all of the unscrambled words.

Sip far

Rude borax

On lay

Miles learn

Cenci

Scene an

In 1999, Time Magazine named Turing as one of the 100 Most Important People of the 20th century.

CONNECTING CLUES

Can you find the connection between all of the
answers by solving the clues below?

Finger joint

Rap on a door

Measure of wind

To be informed or aware

A cutting blade

TURING TEST

Decode this **Alan Turing quote** by cracking the Caesar cipher. Shift each letter a consistent amount forwards or backwards through the alphabet. For example, you might replace A with C, B with D and so on until you replace Y with A and Z with B.

OCA PQV OCEJKPGU ECTTA QWV

UQOGVJKPI YJKEJ QWIJV VQ DG

FGUETKDGF CU VJKPMKPI DWV

YJKEJ KU XGTA FKHHGTGPV

HTQO YJCV C OCP FQGU?

CODE CORNER

Can you decipher the names of these five **Bond villains** which
have each had a particular encryption applied to them?

RESNSTATRVBOOLEFDL

UHOGRDXA

UAIRGCLOFDNIEGR

ELHCFIRFE

ORASLKBEB

PHONETIC CLUES

By saying what you see, reveal the names of each of these **capital cities**.

V N R

X P

L G RR

V N T N

PP O

CONSONANT COMPRESSION

All the vowels, spaces and hyphens have been deleted from the following **types of government**. Some extra spaces have then been inserted to further disguise the original text. Can you restore the missing characters to reveal the original words?

CN STT TN L SM

DC TT RSH P

L GR CHY

TYR N NY

RS TCR CY

MP RL SM

HIDDEN CONNECTION

Each of the following pairs of words secretly conceals
a third word. This third word can be added to the end of
the first word, and the start of the second word, to form
two new words. Can you reveal all six hidden words?

OUT _____ LESS

HEAD _____ RAIN

SUN _____ POT

GRAPE _____ ION

KIN _____ LORE

WILL _____ HOUSE

MISSING CHARACTERS

The following titles of **James Bond** movies are missing all of the letters found in JAMES BOND. Restore the missing letters to reveal the titles.

GLFIGR

CTPUY

GLY

LICC T KILL

FR RUI WITH LV

CI RYL

EXPRESS YOURSELF

Can you re-express each of these five
common phrases?

Snap a femur

Tramps cannot be selective asking for alms

Rather delayed than not at all

A midday meal must be paid for

The premature sparrow eats first

HOMONYM CLUES

Can you find the homonymic connection between all
of the answers by solving the clues below?

Section at the end of a book (8)

Give support to (4)

Punctuation mark preceding a list (5)

Twelve inches (4)

Building devoted to worship (6)

MISSING LETTER

In the following names of **historical figures**, every other letter is missing. Can you fill in the missing letters to reveal the original names?

_I_S_O_ C_U_C_I_L

L_O_ T_O_S_Y

_A_A_M_ G_N_H_

F_O_E_C_ N_G_T_N_A_E

_B_A_A_ L_N_O_N

M_R_I_ L_T_E_ K_N_

*'Codes are a puzzle. A game,
just like any other game.'*

LOGIC PUZZLE

Read the following text and see if you can answer the final question.

Three shapes are drawn in a row on a page. One is a circle, one is a diamond, and one is a rectangle. One is gold, one is silver, and one is bronze. The following is also true:

- The rectangle is next to the bronze shape.

- The diamond is somewhere to the right of the gold shape.

- The metallic shade of the diamond is later in the alphabet than that of the rectangle.

- The left-hand shape has four sides.

Based on this information, can you deduce the metallic shade of each shape, and their relative positions?

HIDDEN WORDS

Can you find the names of five **one-word films** which
have been concealed within the sentences below?

Where has the sugar gone?

An alkali enables an acid to neutralize.

The apartment was chic, a gorgeous wood-
and-glass theme evident throughout.

Don't give the ogre a second thought!

If you don't halt it, an iceberg will hit it.

ANAGRAM + 1

Each of the following lines contains a scrambled word plus one extra letter. These extra letters, when read from top to bottom, will reveal a topic which fits all of the unscrambled words.

A lanky giant

Our praise

Via or tick

I am wale

Ask bail

CONNECTING CLUES

Can you find the connection between all of the
answers by solving the clues below?

Style or category, usually of art

Buttery, flaky pastry

Agreed upon meeting

Business owner or manager

The Nutcracker, eg

TURING TEST

Decode this **Alan Turing quote** by cracking the Caesar cipher. Shift each letter a consistent amount forwards or backwards through the alphabet. For example, you might replace A with C, B with D and so on until you replace Y with A and Z with B.

W YKILQPAN SKQHZ ZAOANRA PK

XA YWHHAZ EJPAHHECAJP EB EP

YKQHZ ZAYAERA W DQIWJ EJPK

XAHEAREJC PDWP EP SWO DQIWJ.

CODE CORNER

Can you decipher the names of these five **Bond actors** which have each had a particular encryption applied to them?

4 1 14 9 5 12 3 18 1 9 7

18 15 7 5 18 13 15 15 18 5

19 5 1 14 3 15 14 14 5 18 25

16 9 5 18 3 5 2 18 15 19 14 1 14

20 9 13 15 20 8 25 4 1 12 20 15 14

PHONETIC CLUES

By saying what you see, reveal the names of each of these **US states**.

10 S E

U ☉ R

N D N R

I O R

A Y E

CONSONANT COMPRESSION

All the vowels, spaces and hyphens have been deleted from the
following **parts of a car**. Some extra spaces have then been
inserted to further disguise the original text. Can you restore
the missing characters to reveal the original words?

CCL RTR

TCHM TR

SP R KPLG

XH STPP

PS TN

BR KPD

HIDDEN CONNECTION

Each of the following pairs of words secretly conceals a third word. This third word can be added to the end of the first word, and the start of the second word, to form two new words. Can you reveal all six hidden words?

PUMP _____ FOLK

OUT _____ WAY

INTER _____ LESS

DATA _____ LINE

UNDER _____ FIELD

GOD _____ BOARD

MISSING CHARACTERS

The following characters from the **Harry Potter books** are missing all of the letters found in HOGWARTS. Restore the missing letters to reveal their names.

LD VLDEM

IIU BLCK

DC MLFY

EVEU NPE

N ELEY

Y PE

'A computer would deserve to be called intelligent if it could deceive a human into believing that it was human.'

EXPRESS YOURSELF

Can you re-express each of these five
common phrases?

History, history, history

To mimic is to excessively
praise without deceit

That which is pleasant is not infinite

Residence is where your
blood gets pumped

Clocks are expensive

HOMONYM CLUES

Can you find the homonymic connection between all
of the answers by solving the clues below?

One that burns fiercely and brightly (6)

People who fight with padded gloves (6)

Brodie, Grey, Harlow and Valjean (5)

Films that are not feature-length (6)

Chanted Scottish girls (10)

MISSING LETTER

In the following names of **birds of prey**, every other letter is missing. Can you fill in the missing letters to reveal the original names?

_U_Z_R_

S_C_E_A_Y _I_D

_A_C_N

O_P_E_

_U_T_R_

G_S_A_K

LOGIC PUZZLE

Read the following text and see if you can answer the final question.

Alex, Billy and Charlie all live on the same street, in three consecutive houses on the odd-numbered side of the street. One lives at number 1, one at number 3 and one at number 5. Each door is a different hue, so one has a blue door, one has a green door and one has a red door. The following is also true:

- Billy lives next to Charlie.

- The house with the blue door is next to Alex's house.

- The resident of number 5 has a name that is later in the alphabet than the resident of the house with the red door.

- Charlie does not have a green door.

Based on this information, can you deduce who lives at which house, and what hue their door is?

HIDDEN WORDS

Can you find the names of five **European countries** which
have been concealed within the sentences below?

We've called Interpol and they can't
give us any new information.

The Bureau's triangulating the data
points from around the city.

Starting that fire landed him in all this trouble.

The wolf ran ceaselessly
through the long grass.

I've spoken about this to his
manager many times.

ANAGRAM + 1

Each of the following lines contains a scrambled word plus one extra letter. These extra letters, when read from top to bottom, will reveal a topic which fits all of the unscrambled words.

Pig or all

Mr rule

A groan unit

Rare mist

Ana bobo

Empathic zen

Big bone

CONNECTING CLUES

Can you find the connection between all of the
answers by solving the clues below?

What this is

To misappropriate money

Whirlpool bath

Winter storm

Off balance and unsteady

TURING TEST

Decode this **Alan Turing quote** by cracking the Caesar cipher.
Shift each letter a consistent amount forwards or backwards
through the alphabet. For example, you might replace A with C,
B with D and so on until you replace Y with A and Z with B.

BJ HFS TSQD XJJ F XMTWY INXYFSHJ

FMJFI, GZY BJ HFS XJJ UQJSYD

YMJWJ YMFY SJJIX YT GJ ITSJ.

CODE CORNER

Can you decipher the names of these five **spy films** which
have each had a particular encryption applied to them?

XZHRML ILBZOV

ZGLNRX YOLMWV

GSV YLFIMV RWVMGRGB

NRHHRLM RNKLHHRYOV

GSV OREVH LU LGSVIH

PHONETIC CLUES

By saying what you see, reveal the names of each of these **flowers**.

M R L S

N M N E

AA A L E R

I R S

P P

Alan Turing essentially founded modern computer science. In 1936, he published a seminal paper called 'On Computable Numbers', which The Washington Post has called 'the founding document of the computer age'.

CONSONANT COMPRESSION

All the vowels, spaces and hyphens have been deleted from the following **styles of martial art**. Some extra spaces have then been inserted to further disguise the original text. Can you restore the missing characters to reveal the original words?

K D

C PR

KN GF

T KW ND

KR T

M YTH

HIDDEN CONNECTION

Each of the following pairs of words secretly conceals
a third word. This third word can be added to the end of
the first word, and the start of the second word, to form
two new words. Can you reveal all six hidden words?

WING _____ TOED

CARP _____ WAY

BAND _____ STILL

KING _____ MAN

CON _____ IONS

OVER _____ PING

MISSING CHARACTERS

The following names of famous **British actors and actresses** are missing all of the letters found in HITCHCOCK. Restore the missing letters to reveal the names.

ANNY PNS

MAEL ANE

AE WNSLE

JN LEESE

ERA NGLEY

RARD BURN

EXPRESS YOURSELF

Can you re-express each of these five
common phrases?

The dollar has a lot to say

Fewer objects result in a greater total count

Requirement is the female parent of creation

Maintain a raised jaw

Avoid executing the envoy

HOMONYM CLUES

Can you find the homonymic connection between all
of the answers by solving the clues below?

Decaying matter of a road vehicle (6)

Space for pulping (8)

Plate of the Egyptian sun god (6)

Crush (6)

Rotate internet protocol (6)

MISSING LETTER

In the following **nursery rhymes**, every other letter is missing. Can you fill in the missing letters to reveal the original rhymes?

_A_ B_A _L_C_S_E_P

C_C_ A _O_D_E _O_

_U_P_Y _U_P_Y

_A_Y _A_ A _I_T_E _A_B

L_T_L_ M_S_ M_F_E_

_H_E_ B_I_D _I_E

LOGIC PUZZLE

Read the following text and see if you can answer the final question.

Three books are stacked in a pile. Each has a different type of cover, with one having a white cover, one a gold cover, and one a black cover. One is 200 pages long, one is 400 pages long, and one is 500 pages long. The following is also true:

- The black book is above the book with 500 pages.

- The book with 200 pages is touching the gold book.

- The middle book has more pages than the white book.

- The top book does not have 400 pages.

Based on this information, can you deduce the position, type of cover, and length of each book?

HIDDEN WORDS

Can you find the names of five **fruits** which have
been concealed within the sentences below?

Were they demons or angels?

They tried to ban an alliance between us.

Sitting by myself all evening
made me lonely and bored.

I imagined I was Holden Caulfield,
catcher, rye and all.

I can only hope a change will come soon.

ANAGRAM + 1

Each of the following lines contains a scrambled word plus one extra letter. These extra letters, when read from top to bottom, will reveal a topic which fits all of the unscrambled words.

Dug a co

Hurry gee

Arch deed

A feet

Oil lush am

A razzle mole

CONNECTING CLUES

Can you find the connection between all of the
answers by solving the clues below?

Nomadic fortune teller, perhaps

Widely held fictitious story

Melodic pattern of sound

Hunter gatherer of short stature

Underground cavity found beneath a church

*'Maths: Not very good. He spends a good
deal of time apparently in investigations in
advanced mathematics to the neglect of his
elementary work. His work is dirty.'*

From Turing's school report, Summer Term 1927

TURING TEST

Decode this **Alan Turing quote** by cracking the Caesar cipher.
Shift each letter a consistent amount forwards or backwards
through the alphabet. For example, you might replace A with C,
B with D and so on until you replace Y with A and Z with B.

RNLDSHLDR HS HR SGD ODNOKD

MN NMD BZM HLZFHMD ZMXSGHMF

NE VGN CN SGD SGHMFR

MN NMD BZM HLZFHMD.

CODE CORNER

Can you decipher the names of these five **intelligence agencies** which have each had a keyboard cipher encryption applied to them?

DGLLQR

LTEKTZ OFZTSSOUTFET LTKCOET

FQZOGFQS LTEXKOZN QUTFEN

UGCTKFDTFZ EGDDXFOEQZOGFL ITQRJXQKZTKL

YTRTKQS WXKTQX GY OFCTLZOUQZOGF

PHONETIC CLUES

By saying what you see, reveal the names of each
of these **plays**, both ancient and modern.

J P P L M

R S TT

LL S TT

U M N A DD

R AA N N[th] S N

CONSONANT COMPRESSION

All the vowels, spaces and hyphens have been deleted from the following **music genres**. Some extra spaces have then been inserted to further disguise the original text. Can you restore the missing characters to reveal the original words?

M BNT

BL GR SS

RG G

G RNG

G S PL

TC H N

HIDDEN CONNECTION

Each of the following pairs of words secretly conceals a third word. This third word can be added to the end of the first word, and the start of the second word, to form two new words. Can you reveal all six hidden words?

SHORT _____ OVER

VIGIL _____ LOPE

FORE _____ PRINT

SEA _____ STUFF

BATTLE _____ WELL

PAR _____ PET

MISSING CHARACTERS

The following names of **Guy Ritchie movies** are missing all of the letters found in GUY RITCHIE. Restore the missing letters to reveal the names.

SNA

SLOK OLMS

VOLV

SSP

SWP AWA

AD AS

EXPRESS YOURSELF

Can you re-express each of these five
common phrases?

Magnetic seduction?

Being frank is the only course worth taking

Eat a watermelon, become a watermelon

Vengeance tastes like candy

You cannot dance alone in Latin America

HOMONYM CLUES

Can you find the homonymic connection between all
of the answers by solving the clues below?

Move forcefully (5)

One that slices (6)

Discarded items (4)

Less heavy (7)

Paintbrush for fine work (5)

MISSING LETTER

In the following **computer accessories**, every other letter is missing. Can you fill in the missing letters to reveal the original words?

_R_N_E_

H_R_ D_I_E

_I_R_P_O_E

K_Y_O_R_

_E_C_M

M_N_T_R

LOGIC PUZZLE

Read the following text and see if you can answer the final question.

There are three puzzles in the paper: a sudoku, a futoshiki and a kakuro. One is easy, one is medium, and one is hard. One is in the top left of the page, one is in the top right, and one is at the bottom. The following is also true:

- The sudoku is harder than the puzzle in the top right.

- The puzzle at the bottom is earlier in the alphabet than the puzzle of medium difficulty.

- The futoshiki is at the top of the page.

Based on this information, can you deduce the position and difficulty of each puzzle?

The Turing Test, proposed by Turing in 1950, suggested that a computer could be said to 'think' if a human being asking it questions could not tell from the answers whether they were conversing with a computer or another human.

HIDDEN WORDS

Can you find the names of five **countries of North America** in the sentences below.

Can a day go by when I don't think of you?

The bear cub attached itself to my arm.

He cooked up an amazing meal for us all.

"Aloha!" they all said, as I walked
in. "Aloha," I timidly replied.

Since I fought with my
co-star I can't get any work.

ANAGRAM + 1

Each of the following lines contains a scrambled word plus one extra letter. These extra letters, when read from top to bottom, will reveal a topic which fits all of the unscrambled words.

Shy pearl

Is able

Mr they

Rancid bore

Len fens

56

CONNECTING CLUES

Can you find the connection between all of the
answers by solving the clues below?

Earth, water, air and fire

Cotton cloud

A monkey's choice of fruit?

Season of heavy rain

Thumbing a lift

TURING TEST

Decode this **Alan Turing quote** by cracking the Caesar cipher.
Shift each letter a consistent amount forwards or backwards
through the alphabet. For example, you might replace A with C,
B with D and so on until you replace Y with A and Z with B.

QB QA XWAAQJTM BW QVDMVB

I AQVOTM UIKPQVM EPQKP KIV

JM CAML BW KWUXCBM IVG

KWUXCBIJTM AMYCMVKM.

58

CODE CORNER

Can you decipher the names of these five **Turing-related words**
which have each had a particular encryption applied to them?

. / _ . / . . / _ _ . / _ _ / . _ /

_ . . . / _ _ _ / _ _ / _ . . . / .

_ . _ . / _ _ _ / _ . . / . / _ . . . /
. _ . / . / . . _ / _ . _ / . / . _ .

_ . . . / . _ . . / . / _ / _ . _ . /
. . . . / . _ . . / . / _ . _ _

_ . _ . / _ _ _ / _ _ / . _ _ . /
. . _ / _ / . . / _ . / _ _ .

PHONETIC CLUES

By saying what you see, reveal the names of
each of these **former countries**.

P DD E R

4 M OO R

Ψ M

N M

N M E D R

CONSONANT COMPRESSION

All the vowels, spaces and hyphens have been deleted from the following **types of poetry**. Some extra spaces have then been inserted to further disguise the original text. Can you restore the missing characters to reveal the original words?

LL GR Y

BL LD

P T PH

L M RCK

H K

P GR M

HIDDEN CONNECTION

Each of the following pairs of words secretly conceals
a third word. This third word can be added to the end of
the first word, and the start of the second word, to form
two new words. Can you reveal all six hidden words?

MASTER _____ LESS

PRO _____ ALLY

SUPER _____ BOARD

UNDER _____ WORD

BASKET _____ ROOMS

SHORT _____ FORM

MISSING CHARACTERS

The following names of **British poets** are missing all of the letters found in MENDING WALL, a Robert Frost poem. Restore the missing letters to reveal the names.

THOS HRY

RUYR KP

JOH TO

Y BROT

CHRST ROSSTT

ZBTH BRRTT BRO

EXPRESS YOURSELF

Can you re-express each of these five
common phrases?

Discourse is on sale

One, two, fortunate

Tally your benedictions

Helium balloons always deflate

Larger groups make it jollier

*'A man provided with paper, pencil, and
rubber, and subject to strict discipline,
is in effect a universal machine.'*

HOMONYM CLUES

Can you find the homonymic connection between all
of the answers by solving the clues below?

The front middle of the body (5)

Put clothes on the Queen (7)

Make fun of smoked meat (7)

Relating to a Turkish dynasty (7)

Garment for a hospital room (8)

ANAGRAMS - 1

Each of these anagrams are missing one letter. The missing letters will spell out another word.

Xi

Rteh

Leene

Tigh

Ein

MISSING LETTER

In the following **classic toys**, every other letter is missing. Can you fill in the missing letters to reveal the original words?

_C_I_N _I_U_E_

B_U_C_ B_L_

_I_S_W

S_I_N_ T_P

_O_K_N_ H_R_E

B_I_D_N_ B_O_K_

LOGIC PUZZLE

Read the following text and see if you can answer the final question.

In a horse race, three horses are leading the pack: 'Rein of Terror', 'Hot to Trot', and 'The Mane Event'. One of these horses has a white coat, one a chestnut coat, and one a black coat. The following is also true:

- Hot to Trot is a place behind the white horse.

- The horse in second place has a name that is earlier in the alphabet (including any 'The' in the horse's name, if appropriate) than the chestnut horse.

- The black horse is not between the other two.

Based on this information, can you deduce the position and coat of each horse?

HIDDEN WORDS

Can you find the names of five **birds** which have
been concealed within the sentences below?

How long does it take to develop a habit?

I tapped her on the arm.

I'd like to ski with no poles.

At the river I met a fast-talking
fisherman with a can of worms.

I knocked down my brother's
wall, owing to the damp.

ANAGRAM + 1

Each of the following lines contains a scrambled word plus one extra letter. These extra letters, when read from top to bottom, will reveal a topic which fits all of the unscrambled words.

A phrase keeps

Toy sea

Cumin Gems

Wilted

Slim ton

CONNECTING CLUES

Can you find the connection between all of the
answers by solving the clues below?

Organ of sight

Container often made of woven material

Artillery mounted on wheels

Arc

Ice crystals

TURING TEST

Decode this **Alan Turing quote** by cracking the Caesar cipher. Shift each letter a consistent amount forwards or backwards through the alphabet. For example, you might replace A with C, B with D and so on until you replace Y with A and Z with B.

JXZEFKBP QXHB JB YV PROMOFPB

TFQE DOBXQ COBNRBKZV.

CODE CORNER

Can you decipher the names of these five **fictional spies** which
have each had a particular encryption applied to them?

24 11 43 34 33 12 34 45 42 33 15

22 15 34 42 22 15 43 32 24 31 15 54

15 51 15 31 54 33 43 11 31 44

24 11 32 15 43 12 34 33 14

24 11 13 25 42 54 11 33

PHONETIC CLUES

By saying what you see, reveal the names of each of these **novels**.

M R

U L S EE

8 L F 2 C TT

N R K R N N R

N P M NN R

Turing's codebreaking machine the Bombe shortened the steps required in the decoding process, allowing the Bletchley Park codebreakers to decipher up to 4000 messages a day.

CONSONANT COMPRESSION

All the vowels, spaces and hyphens have been deleted from the following **extinct animals**. Some extra spaces have then been inserted to further disguise the original text. Can you restore the missing characters to reveal the original names?

R CHS

T HY LC N

W LL Y M MMT H

QG G

D D

M GL D N

HIDDEN CONNECTION

Each of the following pairs of words secretly conceals
a third word. This third word can be added to the end of
the first word, and the start of the second word, to form
two new words. Can you reveal all six hidden words?

WORK _____ SPACE

VIGIL _____ EATER

IMP _____ IONS

WHOLE _____ MEN

CAR _____ TING

RAIN _____ OUT

MISSING CHARACTERS

The following names of **children's authors** are missing all of the letters found in WINNIE THE POOH. Restore the missing letters to reveal the names.

RALD DAL

L ULLMA

BARX R

D BLY

JACQUL LS

JULA DALDS

EXPRESS YOURSELF

Can you re-express each of these five
common phrases?

Activities are noisier than squabbles

Mention Lucifer

Below atmospheric conditions

Inquisitiveness executed Garfield?

To be unaware is to be joyful

HOMONYM CLUES

Can you find the homonymic connection between all
of the answers by solving the clues below?

A pain in the neck (5)

Aggressive dog, that is to say (5)

Hunting game with a trained bird of prey (7)

Adore patterned silk (8)

Modern unit of weight (6)

MISSING LETTER

In the following names of **philosophers,** every other letter is missing.
Can you fill in the missing letters to reveal the original names?

_R_S_O_L_

C_O_S_Y

_I_T_S_H_

R_U_S_A_

_A_T_E

L_I_N_Z

LOGIC PUZZLE

Read the following text and see if you can answer the final question.

Three ships are sailing to England: the Deliverance, the Odyssey, and the Triumph. One is docking at Cowes, one at Dover, and one at Newhaven. One is arriving at one o'clock, one at two o'clock, and one at three o'clock. The following is also true:

- The Deliverance is docking after the ship that is docking at Dover.

- The ship docking at Cowes has a name that is later in the alphabet than the ship docking at one o'clock.

- The ship docking at Newhaven is docking at an odd-numbered hour.

Based on this information, can you deduce the time and place of the docking of each ship?

HIDDEN WORDS

Can you find the names of five **types of shoes** which
have been concealed within the sentences below?

The company had a very basic logo.

The builders at the spa drilled for
the duration of my treatment.

I tried to comb rogue hairs
away from my face.

Just three minutes and already
you're getting on my nerves!

The top of his lip perspired in the heat.

ANAGRAM + 1

Each of the following lines contains a scrambled word plus one extra letter. These extra letters, when read from top to bottom, will reveal a topic which fits all of the unscrambled words.

Som mue

An old hip

Plan theme

Wheel album

Rules iraq

Verb ale

The chase

CONNECTING CLUES

Can you find the connection between all of the
answers by solving the clues below?

Smokey haze

Late morning meal

Continental area from Iceland to Japan

Episodic funny TV show

Overnight accommodation for motorists

*'It is possible to invent a single
machine which can be used to
compute any computable sequence.'*

TURING TEST

Decode this **Alan Turing quote** by cracking the Caesar cipher. Shift each letter a consistent amount forwards or backwards through the alphabet. For example, you might replace A with C, B with D and so on until you replace Y with A and Z with B.

H THU WYVCPKLK DPAO WHWLY,

WLUJPS, HUK YBIILY, HUK ZBIQLJA

AV ZAYPJA KPZJPWSPUL, PZ PU

LMMLJA H BUPCLYZHS THJOPUL.

CODE CORNER

Can you decipher the names of these five **Bond theme performers** by applying a keyword-based cipher to them? The keyword is SOUNDTRACK, but it is up to you to work out how to apply it.

NQLSG NQLSG

FSNHGGS

MACLDY OSMMDY

GSGUY MCGSPLS

PHF KHGDM

PHONETIC CLUES

By saying what you see, reveal the names of each of these **drinks**.

T

B R

P P A

P N O N R

T R M E R

CONSONANT COMPRESSION

All the vowels, spaces and hyphens have been deleted from the following **Renaissance artists**. Some extra spaces have then been inserted to further disguise the original text. Can you restore the missing characters to reveal the original names?

B TT CL L

D V NC

RP H L

M CHL N GL

DNT L L

B SC H

HIDDEN CONNECTION

Each of the following pairs of words secretly conceals a third word. This third word can be added to the end of the first word, and the start of the second word, to form two new words. Can you reveal all six hidden words?

GAS _____ HOP

PEA _____ SHELLS

SHIP _____ STICKS

HERE _____ SHAVE

KEY _____ WORTHY

FOR _____ GREEN

MISSING CHARACTERS

The following names of **Shakespeare plays** are missing
all of the letters found in SHAKESPEARE. Restore
the missing letters to reveal the names.

MCBT

T TMT

NY V

ING L

MLT

T WINT' TL

EXPRESS YOURSELF

Can you re-express each of these five
common phrases?

Crack the whisky rocks?

You won't find currency on sycamores

Affection is requiring braille

If a sundial grew wings and took to the skies

Chew the slug

HOMONYM CLUES

Can you find the homonymic connection between all
of the answers by solving the clues below?

Feline sharing a name with Turing (7)

Male makes beer (6)

Small citrus fruit (8)

Make smooth and shiny (6)

McKellen as an ancient Italian? (8)

MISSING LETTER

In the following **geographical features**, every other letter is missing.
Can you fill in the missing letters to reveal the original words?

_R_H_P_L_G_

P_N_N_U_A

_U_D_A

S_V_N_A_

_I_E_B_D

G_A_I_R

LOGIC PUZZLE

Read the following text and see if you can answer the final question.

Three different cars were parked outside an office this week. One had navy blue paint, one had silver paint, and one had white paint. One was a Nissan, one was a Renault, and one was a Toyota. One was parked there on Monday, one on Tuesday, and one on Wednesday. The following is also true:

- The navy car was parked outside the office after the Nissan.

- The brand of the silver car is earlier in the alphabet than the brand of a car parked on Monday.

- The white car is not a Toyota.

Based on this information, can you deduce the paint and brand of each car, and the day it was parked outside the office?

Alan Turing had a reputation for eccentricities. Instead of mending a faulty bicycle chain, he used to count his pedal strokes and get off the bicycle to adjust the chain before it was due to come off.

94

HIDDEN WORDS

Can you find the names of five **countries of Asia** which
have been concealed within the sentences below?

The agent sat on the bench in a
trench coat and dark glasses.

I ran away as fast as I could.

Out of the corner of my eye men in trench
coats appeared from all sides, closing in.

Fleeing the unfamiliar men, I attempted
to climb up a nearby tree.

The last thing I heard was a
thin, diabolical laugh.

ANAGRAM + 1

Each of the following lines contains a scrambled word plus one extra letter. These extra letters, when read from top to bottom, will reveal a topic which fits all of the unscrambled words.

Net sins

Balk best pal

Core tick

Bar labels

Try bug

Flogs

96

CONNECTING CLUES

Can you find the connection between all of the
answers by solving the clues below?

Less heavy

Evidence of truth

Place of employment

Timber

Insect of the genus Musca

TURING TEST

Decode this **Alan Turing quote** by cracking the Caesar cipher.
Shift each letter a consistent amount forwards or backwards
through the alphabet. For example, you might replace A with C,
B with D and so on until you replace Y with A and Z with B.

OCJNZ RCJ XVI DHVBDIZ VITOCDIB,

XVI XMZVOZ OCZ DHKJNNDWGZ.

CODE CORNER

Can you decipher the names of these five **Bond novels** which
have each had a binary encryption applied to them?

111 1111 1100 100 110 1001 1110 111 101 10010

1101 1111 1111 1110 10010 1 1011 101 10010

10100 1000 10101 1110 100 101
10010 10 1 1100 1100

11001 1111 10101   1111 1110 1100 11001
1100 1001 10110 101   10100 10111 1001 11 101

1100 1001 10110 101   1 1110 100
1100 101 10100   100 1001 101

PHONETIC CLUES

By saying what you see, reveal the names
of each of these **types of pasta**.

RR O

G M L E

Φ 2 X N E

4 4 L R

R A K T

CONSONANT COMPRESSION

All the vowels, spaces and hyphens have been deleted from the following **pieces of medical equipment**. Some extra spaces have then been inserted to further disguise the original text. Can you restore the missing characters to reveal the original words?

P CMK R

T RN QT

S YRN G

DF B RLL TR

FR CP S

C T HTR

HIDDEN CONNECTION

Each of the following pairs of words secretly conceals
a third word. This third word can be added to the end of
the first word, and the start of the second word, to form
two new words. Can you reveal all six hidden words?

UNDER _____ ROOMS

SURE _____ BRAND

TAB _____ DOWN

BALL _____ WAY

MOON _____ HEARTED

SOME _____ WORK

102

MISSING CHARACTERS

The following names of **Dickens novels** are missing all of the letters found in CHARLES DICKENS. Restore the missing letters to reveal the names.

OV TWT

V OPPF

B OU

T PW PP

OU MUTU F

T BTT OF F

EXPRESS YOURSELF

Can you re-express each of these five
common phrases?

Rhythmic occurrence surrounding
wild Australian country

Removing angled edges of a square

Punch the pouch

The final stalk of grain

Yearn for the gravy vessel

HOMONYM CLUES

Can you find the homonymic connection between all
of the answers by solving the clues below?

One who rolls a ball and
knocks down pins (6)

Go past in public transport vehicle (5)

One who follows hoofed animals (11)

A Moroccan city (3)

More serious letter after N (8)

MISSING LETTER

In the following **currencies**, every other letter is missing. Can you fill in the missing letters to reveal the original words?

_A_T

D_A_H_A

_A_D

S_E_E_

_U_L_E_

R_A_

LOGIC PUZZLE

Read the following text and see if you can answer the final question.

The band Hemlock have released four albums: Bronze Lows, Fighter, Sleep Well, and The Shadows Approach. One is 47 minutes long, one is 58 minutes, one is 65 minutes, and one is 78 minutes. The following is also true:

- Bronze Lows is longer than the third album to be released.

- The most recent album has a two-word title.

- The 65-minute album was released before The Shadows Approach.

- The second album to be released has a name that is earlier in the alphabet than the name of the 78-minute album.

- Fighter is shorter than the second album to be released.

- The first album to be released is not 58 minutes long.

Based on this information, can you deduce the order in which the albums came out, and the length of each one?

HIDDEN WORDS

Can you find the names of five **artists** which have
been concealed within the sentences below?

He changed the topic as soon as he could.

She had a lot of wisdom on eternal life.

'Look! Ah, look!' I said, pointing
at the spectacle.

The diplomat is secretly stealing information.

A strange feeling came over
me, eradicating my fear.

ANAGRAM + 1

Each of the following lines contains a scrambled word plus one extra letter. These extra letters, when read from top to bottom, will reveal a topic which fits all of the unscrambled words.

We trim book

Boot a helium

Bye cecil

Core toes

Whole brawler

Rare bells sold

CONNECTING CLUES

Can you find the connection between all of the
answers by solving the clues below?

A boat of Inuit origin

Midday

Each stage in a video game

Title of mistress of the house

A system of detection used to
locate ships and aircraft

TURING TEST

Decode this **Alan Turing quote** by cracking the Caesar cipher.
Shift each letter a consistent amount forwards or backwards
through the alphabet. For example, you might replace A with C,
B with D and so on until you replace Y with A and Z with B.

UR M YMOTUZQ UE QJBQOFQP

FA NQ UZRMXXUNXQ, UF OMZZAF

MXEA NQ UZFQXXUSQZF.

CODE CORNER

Can you decipher the names of these five
spies which have each had a particular character-
set encryption applied to them?

86 105 114 103 105 110 105 97 32 72 97 108 108

83 105 100 110 101 121 32 82
101 105 108 108 121

74 97 109 101 115 32 65 114 109
105 115 116 101 97 100

77 97 116 97 32 72 97 114 105

71 105 97 99 111 109 111 32 67
97 115 97 110 111 118 97

PHONETIC CLUES

By saying what you see, can you reveal the
names of each of these **singers**?

B NN A

L VV P R S L E

JJ 10 B B R

X L P P

N E L N X

CONSONANT COMPRESSION

All the vowels, spaces and hyphens have been deleted from the following **parts of the brain**. Some extra spaces have then been inserted to further disguise the original text. Can you restore the missing characters to reveal the original words?

M YG DL

CR BR LCR TX

HI P PCM PS

F RNT LL B

M DLL BL N GT

P TT RY GLN D

HIDDEN CONNECTION

Each of the following pairs of words secretly conceals
a third word. This third word can be added to the end of
the first word, and the start of the second word, to form
two new words. Can you reveal all six hidden words?

MAIN _____ WORK

TYPE _____ WRITER

ANT _____ SIDE

SKULL _____ ABILITY

OVER _____ AWED

HARD _____ ALL

MISSING CHARACTERS

The following names of **characters from Charlotte Brontë novels** are missing all of the letters found in JANE EYRE. Restore the missing letters to reveal the names.

BLCH IGM

DWD OCHST

DL VS

BTH MSO

GC POOL

LIZ D

EXPRESS YOURSELF

Can you re-express each of these five
common phrases?

Situated in the area immediately above
the round kicking-and-throwing object

Tugging the support of your table

Felines and canines are being
created from condensation

Growling skyward at the oak, not the willow

The price of two body parts

HOMONYM CLUES

Can you find the homonymic connection between all
of the answers by solving the clues below?

Tree material opposite the west (8)

Fasten male bird (9)

Absence of computer network (5)

Sailor and social insect in nothing (9)

Floating glacier male (7)

MISSING LETTER

In the following **natural wonders of the world**, every other letter is missing. Can you fill in the missing letters to reveal the original wonders?

_M_Z_N _A_N_O_E_T

K_M_D_ I_L_N_

_A_L_ M_U_T_I_

H_ L_N_ B_Y

_O_N_ K_L_M_N_A_O

LOGIC PUZZLE

Read the following text and see if you can answer the final question.

Four spies are undercover in Europe. Their codenames are Crow, Eagle, Falcon and Raven. One is undercover in Amsterdam, one in Berlin, one in London and one in Paris. One has been undercover for a week, one for a fortnight, one for a month and one for six months. The following is also true:

- Eagle has been undercover for longer than the spy in Paris.

- Falcon has been undercover for more than a fortnight.

- The spy that has been undercover for a week has a name that is earlier in the alphabet than the spy that is in Amsterdam.

- The spy in Berlin has been undercover for longer than the spy in London.

- The spy in Amsterdam has been undercover for longer than Falcon.

- The city Raven is in has a name the same length as the city of the spy who has been undercover for a week.

Based on this information, can you deduce the codename and location of each spy, and how long they have been undercover?

HIDDEN WORDS

Can you find the names of five **Greek gods** which have
been concealed within the sentences below?

She tries to amaze us with her wild stories.

She recounts the drama, then
asks us what we think.

We give her a couple of
comments and remarks.

We are slightly too brief to convince her.

I suppose I don't need to say
anything particularly profound.

ANAGRAM + 1

Each of the following lines contains a scrambled word plus one extra letter. These extra letters, when read from top to bottom, will reveal a topic which fits all of the unscrambled words.

Happier gross

Blind yard

Sec trick

Flutter bye

Elect be

Meet bubble

Ant miss

CONNECTING CLUES

Can you find the connection between all of the
answers by solving the clues below?

Without a doubt

To illegally seize control of a vehicle in transit

Arts and history museum
located in Amsterdam

Former name of the capital city of Turkey

Well known German pork sausage

TURING TEST

Decode this **Alan Turing quote** by cracking the Caesar cipher. Shift each letter a consistent amount forwards or backwards through the alphabet. For example, you might replace A with C, B with D and so on until you replace Y with A and Z with B.

MU QHU DEJ YDJUHUIJUT YD JXU

VQSJ JXQJ JXU RHQYD XQI JXU

SEDIYIJUDSO EV SEBT FEHHYTWU.

CODE CORNER

Can you decipher the names of these five **spy authors** which have
had a particular hexadecimal encryption applied to them?

4a 6f 68 6e 20 4c 65 20 43 61 72 72 65

49 61 6e 20 46 6c 65 6d 69 6e 67

47 72 61 68 61 6d 20 47 72 65 65 6e 65

52 6f 62 65 72 74 20 4c 75 64 6c 75 6d

4b 65 6e 20 46 6f 6c 6c 65 74 74

PHONETIC CLUES

By saying what you see, reveal the names of
each of these **bodies of water**.

KK P N C

N D N OO N

R A B N C

M AA N (R E 4)

A G N C

CONSONANT COMPRESSION

All the vowels, spaces and hyphens have been deleted from the following **gemstones**. Some extra spaces have then been inserted to further disguise the original text. Can you restore the missing characters to reveal the original words?

TR M LN

TR Q S

ML CHT

L PS LZ L

B SDN

C TR N

HIDDEN CONNECTION

Each of the following pairs of words secretly conceals
a third word. This third word can be added to the end of
the first word, and the start of the second word, to form
two new words. Can you reveal all six hidden words?

TIP _____ NAIL

TYPO _____ ALLY

DON _____ STROKE

GRAPE _____ YARD

WITH _____ BACK

COOK _____ SMART

MISSING CHARACTERS

The following **locations in the titles of Agatha Christie novels** are missing all of the letters found in AGATHA CHRISTIE. Restore the missing letters to reveal the names.

MOPOM

NL

BDD

BBN

FNKFU

ON

EXPRESS YOURSELF

Can you re-express each of these five
common phrases?

Smash the tack on the upper body part

A portion of birthday dessert?

Untamed waterfowl pursuit

Larger salmon to sauté

Provide a small coin for the
results of your cogitation

LOGIC PUZZLE

Read the following text and see if you can answer the final question.

There is a double agent working in the secret service. A gunfight has resulted in the death of agent Green, and four agents are in the wind: Blue, Orange, Pink and Red. Each of these four agents has a different make of gun: one has a Beretta, one a Colt, one a Glock and one a Walther. They also use four different sizes of bullet: one 2mm bullets, one 3mm bullets, one 4mm and one 6mm. The bullet wounds are characteristic of a Glock. The following is also true:

- The owner of the Walther uses bigger bullets than Red.

- The user of 4mm bullets has a longer codename than the user of the Beretta.

- Pink's bullets are half the size of Orange's bullets.

- The Glock uses an even-numbered bullet size.

- Orange has a longer gun brand name than Pink.

- The owner of the Walther has a codename that is later in the alphabet than the owner of the Beretta.

Based on this information, can you deduce which agent uses which gun and which bullets, and thus deduce who shot agent Green?

HIDDEN WORDS

Can you find the names of five **African countries** which
have been concealed within the sentences below?

There's nowhere left to go.

She gave me a malignant smile.

If you're busy now, maybe we can go later.

She pointed the elder wand at me
with a fierce glint in her eye.

Would you rather watch a
romcom or Oscar bait?

ANAGRAM + 1

Each of the following lines contains a scrambled word plus one extra letter. These extra letters, when read from top to bottom, will reveal a topic which fits all of the unscrambled words.

Some mucky ice

A snubby gun

Eye prop

Knot clad dud

Towy tee

Toot cam

Pen bog snob

CONNECTING CLUES

Can you find the connection between all of the
answers by solving the clues below?

Occurring now

Official authorization, eg for fishing

To dispute or call into question

Instrument used by referee

A disrespectful or offensive criticism

TURING TEST

Decode this **Alan Turing quote** by cracking the Caesar cipher. Shift each letter a consistent amount forwards or backwards through the alphabet. For example, you might replace A with C, B with D and so on until you replace Y with A and Z with B.

DNTPYNP TD L OTQQPCPYETLW

PBFLETZY. CPWTRTZY TD L

MZFYOLCJ NZYOTETZY.

CODE CORNER

Can you decipher the names of these five **opening lines of Bond novels** which have each had a rail fence encryption applied to them? It is up to you to work out how many rails are required. Can you also then say which novel these lines come from?

IRIWWSUNNAAANGY

TCAMA WOAON ENTEH RGHSE TNSOE NSETF
CSNAE ASAIGT HEITE ONNEN DKDAA IRUTARNMI

TYEDW BKBOE RLFTH EEBHN TEIEL CRBEG
GLSEE ODSLN ESIHD AURGWCAI

TEMNF AXIEE SEEHR AEOET OGETU
UYNHL FOAER TGNER MSRL RTIFCAT

TWIET ASLEL HTOHR YIHSO RDIUT
NOSYE TTGRE MAU

PHONETIC CLUES

By saying what you see, reveal the names
of each of these **US presidents**.

II N O R

K N A D

AA

P RR S

J 44 N

MISSING LETTER

In the following **musical instruments**, every other letter is missing.
Can you fill in the missing letters to reveal the original words?

A_C_R_I_N

_A_P_S

C_N_E_T_N_

_L_C_E_S_I_L

D_D_E_I_O_

_A_O_H_N_

1.

- Austen: My be<u>au sten</u>cilled a floral design.
- Woolf: I bought <u>wool,</u> forgetting that my needles were broken.
- Forster: We washed our hands <u>for sterilization.</u>
- Rowling: Tomor<u>row, ling</u>uists will lecture us about speech development.
- Shelley: I observed the beautiful <u>shell, eyes</u> wide with admiration.

2.

- Lombard Road has water works for a week.
- Merton Road has gas works for a month.
- New Park Road has electricity works for two weeks.

3.

The connecting word is FRANCE
Paris
Bordeaux
Lyon
Marseille
Nice
Cannes

4.

The connection is SILENT K
Knuckle
Knock
Knot
Knowledgeable
Knife

5.

May not machines carry out something which ought to be described as thinking but which is very different from what a man does?

6.

Pairs of consecutive letters have been swapped, and spaces removed
- ERNST STAVRO BLOFELD
- HUGO DRAX
- AURIC GOLDFINGER
- LE CHIFFRE
- ROSA KLEBB

7.

VIENNA
CAIRO (using Greek letters)
ALGIERS
VIENTIANE
ROSEAU (with two Greek letters)

8.

CONSTITUTIONALISM
DICTATORSHIP
OLIGARCHY
TYRANNY
ARISTOCRACY
IMPERIALISM

9.

- BOUND: OUTBOUND and BOUNDLESS
- REST: HEADREST and RESTRAIN
- FLOWER: SUNFLOWER and FLOWERPOT
- FRUIT: GRAPEFRUIT and FRUITION
- FOLK: KINFOLK and FOLKLORE
- POWER: WILLPOWER and POWERHOUSE

10.
GOLDFINGER
OCTOPUSSY
GOLDENEYE
LICENCE TO KILL
FROM RUSSIA WITH LOVE
CASINO ROYALE

11.
Break a leg
Beggars can't be choosers
Better safe than sorry
There's no such thing as a free lunch
The early bird gets the worm

12.
The connection is PARTS OF THE BODY
Appendix
Back
Colon
Foot
Temple

13.
WINSTON CHURCHILL
LEON TROTSKY
MAHATMA GANDHI
FLORENCE NIGHTINGALE
ABRAHAM LINCOLN
MARTIN LUTHER KING

14.
- The rectangle is gold and on the left.
- The circle is bronze and in the middle.
- The diamond is silver and on the right.

15.
Argo
Alien
Chicago
Grease
Titanic

16.
The connecting word is LAKES
Tanganyika
Superior
Victoria
Malawi
Baikal

17.
The connection is FRENCH ORIGIN
Genre
Croissant
Rendezvous
Entrepreneur
Ballet

18.
A computer would deserve to be called intelligent if it could deceive a human into believing that it was human.

19.
Each letter of the alphabet has been replaced by its position within the alphabet, so 1=A, 2=B, etc
- DANIEL CRAIG
- ROGER MOORE
- SEAN CONNERY
- PIERCE BROSNAN
- TIMOTHY DALTON

20.

TENNESSEE
UTAH
INDIANA
IOWA
HAWAII

21.

ACCELERATOR
TACHOMETER
SPARK PLUG
EXHAUST PIPE
PISTON
BRAKE PAD

22.

- KIN: PUMPKIN and KINFOLK
- RUN: OUTRUN and RUNWAY
- FACE: INTERFACE and FACELESS
- BASE: DATABASE and BASELINE
- MINE: UNDERMINE and MINEFIELD
- MOTHER: GODMOTHER and MOTHERBOARD

23.

LORD VOLDEMORT
SIRIUS BLACK
DRACO MALFOY
SEVERUS SNAPE
RON WEASLEY
HARRY POTTER

24.

History repeats itself
Imitation is the sincerest form of flattery
Good things come to an end
Home is where the heart is
Time is money

25.

The connection is ITEMS OF CLOTHING

- Blazer
- Boxers
- Jeans
- Shorts
- Sunglasses: sung lasses

26.

BUZZARD
SECRETARY BIRD
FALCON
OSPREY
VULTURE
GOSHAWK

27.

- Alex lives at number 1 with a red door.
- Billy lives at number 5 with a green door.
- Charlie lives at number 3 with a blue door.

28.

Poland
Austria
Ireland
France
Germany

29.

The connecting word is PRIMATE
Gorilla
Lemur
Orangutan
Tarsier
Baboon
Chimpanzee
Gibbon

30.

The connection is DOUBLE Z

Puzzle

Embezzle

Jacuzzi

Blizzard

Dizzy

31.

We can only see a short distance ahead, but we can see plenty there that needs to be done.

32.

An Atbash cipher has been applied, so A has been replaced with Z and vice-versa, B has been replaced with Y and vice-versa, and so on

- CASINO ROYALE
- ATOMIC BLONDE
- THE BOURNE IDENTITY
- MISSION IMPOSSIBLE
- THE LIVES OF OTHERS

33.

AMARYLLIS

ANEMONE

AZALEA

IRIS

ROSE

34.

AIKIDO

CAPOEIRA

KUNG FU

TAE KWON DO

KARATE

MUAY THAI

35.

- TIP: WINGTIP and TIPTOED
- ENTRY: CARPENTRY and ENTRYWAY
- STAND: BANDSTAND and STANDSTILL
- FISHER: KINGFISHER and FISHERMAN
- QUEST: CONQUEST and QUESTIONS
- LAP: OVERLAP and LAPPING

36.

ANTHONY HOPKINS

MICHAEL CAINE

KATE WINSLET

JOHN CLEESE

KEIRA KNIGHTLEY

RICHARD BURTON

37.

Money talks

Less is more

Necessity is the mother of invention

Keep your chin up

Don't shoot the messenger

38.

The connection is VEGETABLES

- Carrot: car rot
- Mushroom: mush room
- Radish: Ra dish
- Squash: squash
- Turnip: turn IP

39.

BAA BAA BLACK SHEEP
COCK A DOODLE DOO
HUMPTY DUMPTY
MARY HAD A LITTLE LAMB
LITTLE MISS MUFFET
THREE BLIND MICE

40.

- The bottom book is white with 400 pages.
- The middle book is gold with 500 pages.
- The top book is black with 200 pages.

41.

Orange
Banana
Melon
Cherry
Peach

42.

The connecting word is CHEESE
Gouda
Gruyere
Cheddar
Feta
Halloumi
Mozzarella

43.

The connection is NO VOWELS
Gypsy
Myth
Rhythm
Pygmy
Crypt

44.

Sometimes it is the people no one can imagine anything of who do the things no one can imagine.

45.

Reading the letters of a standard QWERTY keyboard from left-to-right, top-to-bottom, change Q to A, W to B, E to C, R to D and so on

- MOSSAD
- SECRET INTELLIGENCE SERVICE
- NATIONAL SECURITY AGENCY
- GOVERNMENT COMMUNICATIONS HEADQUARTERS
- FEDERAL BUREAU OF INVESTIGATION

46.

JERUSALEM
ORESTES
ALCESTIS
EUMENIDES
A RAISIN IN THE SUN

47.

AMBIENT
BLUEGRASS
REGGAE
GRUNGE
GOSPEL
TECHNO

48.

- CHANGE: SHORTCHANGE and CHANGEOVER
- ANTE: VIGILANTE and ANTELOPE
- FINGER: FOREFINGER and FINGERPRINT
- FOOD: SEAFOOD and FOODSTUFF
- GROUNDS: BATTLEGROUNDS and GROUNDSWELL
- SNIP: PARSNIP and SNIPPET

49.

SNATCH
SHERLOCK HOLMES
REVOLVER
SUSPECT
SWEPT AWAY
THE HARD CASE

50.

Opposites attract
Honesty is the best policy
You are what you eat
Revenge is sweet
It takes two to tango

51.

The connection is BOATS
- Barge
- Cutter
- Junk
- Lighter
- Liner

52.

PRINTER
HARD DRIVE
MICROPHONE
KEYBOARD
WEBCAM
MONITOR

53.

- The sudoku is medium and in the top left.
- The futoshiki is easy and in the top right.
- The kakuro is hard and at the bottom

54.

Canada
Cuba
Panama
Haiti
Costa Rica

55.

The connecting word is HERBS
Parsley
Basil
Thyme
Coriander
Fennel

56.

The connection is ONLY ONE TYPE OF VOWEL
Elements
Cumulus
Banana
Monsoon
Hitch-hiking

57.

It is possible to invent a single machine which can be used to compute any computable sequence.

58.

Each letter has been replaced by its corresponding Morse Code letter, with a '/' indicating a new letter

- ENIGMA
- BOMBE
- CODEBREAKER
- BLETCHLEY
- COMPUTING

59.

RHODESIA
FORMOSA
SIAM
ANNAM
NUMIDIA

60.

ALLEGORY
BALLADE
EPITAPH
LIMERICK
HAIKU
EPIGRAM

61.

- MIND: MASTERMIND and MINDLESS
- VERB: PROVERB and VERBALLY
- STAR: SUPERSTAR and STARBOARD
- PASS: UNDERPASS and PASSWORD
- BALL: BASKETBALL and BALLROOMS
- WAVE: SHORTWAVE and WAVEFORM

62.

THOMAS HARDY
RUDYARD KIPLING
JOHN MILTON
EMILY BRONTE
CHRISTINA ROSSETTI
ELIZABETH BARRETT BROWNING

63.

Talk is cheap
Third time lucky
Count your blessings
What goes up must come down
The more the merrier

64.

The connection is FURNITURE

- Chest
- Dresser: dress ER
- Hammock: ham mock
- Ottoman
- Wardrobe: ward robe

65.

The connecting word is SEVEN
Six
Three
Eleven
Eight
Nine

66.
ACTION FIGURES
BOUNCY BALL
JIGSAW
SPINNING TOP
ROCKING HORSE
BUILDING BLOCKS

67.
- The Mane Event is chestnut and is in first place.
- Rein of Terror is white and is in second place.
- Hot to Trot is black and in third place.

68.
Owl
Heron
Kiwi
Kingfisher
Swallow

69.
The connecting word is POETS
Shakespeare
Yeats
Cummings
Wilde
Milton

70.
The connection is BALL
Eye
Basket
Cannon
Curve
Snow

71.
Machines take me by surprise with great frequency.

72.
A Polybius Square encryption has been applied, so the first digit of each number reveals a set of letters (A to E, F to K, L to P etc) and the second digit indexes into it. As usual in a Polybius Square, I and J share the value 24.
- JASON BOURNE
- GEORGE SMILEY
- EVELYN SALT
- JAMES BOND
- JACK RYAN

73.
EMMA
ULYSSES
A TALE OF TWO CITIES
ANNA KARENINA
NEUROMANCER

74.
AUROCHS
THYLACINE
WOOLLY MAMMOTH
QUAGGA
DODO
MEGALODON

75.
- LOAD: WORKLOAD and LOADSPACE
- ANT: VIGILANT and ANTEATER
- ACT: IMPACT and ACTIONS
- SALES: WHOLESALES and SALESMEN
- PET: CARPET and PETTING
- DROP: RAINDROP and DROPOUT

76.

ROALD DAHL
PHILIP PULLMAN
BEATRIX POTTER
ENID BLYTON
JACQUELINE WILSON
JULIA DONALDSON

77.

Actions speak louder than words
Speak of the devil
Under the weather
Curiosity killed the cat
Ignorance is bliss

78.

The connection is SCIENTISTS
- Crick
- Curie: cur, ie
- Hawking
- Lovelac: love lace
- Newton: new ton

79.

ARISTOTLE
CHOMSKY
NIETZSCHE
ROUSSEAU
SARTRE
LEIBNIZ

80.

- The Deliverance is docking at three o'clock at Newhaven.
- The Odyssey is docking at one o'clock at Dover.
- The Triumph is docking at two o'clock at Cowes.

81.

Clog
Espadrille
Brogue
Sandal
Slipper

82.

The connecting word is MAMMALS
Mouse
Dolphin
Elephant
Blue Whale
Squirrel
Beaver
Cheetah

83.

The connection is PORTMANTEAU
Smog
Brunch
Eurasia
Sitcom
Motel

84.

A man provided with paper, pencil, and rubber, and subject to strict discipline, is in effect a universal machine.

85.

The letters of the keyword must be changed, in order, to A to J, and then the letters of the alphabet not used in SOUNDTRACK should be converted to K to Z in alphabetical order

- DURAN DURAN
- MADONNA
- SHIRLEY BASSEY
- NANCY SINATRA
- TOM JONES

86.

TEA
BEER
ROSÉ
PINOT NOIR
TIA MARIA

87.

BOTTICELLI
DA VINCI
RAPHAEL
MICHELANGELO
DONATELLO
BOSCH

88.

- WORKS: GASWORKS and WORKSHOP
- NUT: PEANUT and NUTSHELLS
- YARD: SHIPYARD and YARDSTICKS
- AFTER: HEREAFTER and AFTERSHAVE
- NOTE: KEYNOTE and NOTEWORTHY
- EVER: FOREVER and EVERGREEN

89.

MACBETH
THE TEMPEST
HENRY V
KING LEAR
HAMLET
THE WINTER'S TALE

90.

Break the ice
Money doesn't grow on trees
Love is blind
Time flies
Bite the bullet

91.

The connection is LANGUAGES

- Catalan: cat Alan
- Hebre: he brew
- Mandarin
- Polish
- Romanian: Roman Ian

92.

ARCHIPELAGO
PENINSULA
TUNDRA
SAVANNAH
RIVERBED
GLACIER

93.

- The navy blue car was a Toyota and was parked outside the office on Wednesday.
- The silver car was a Nissan and was parked outside the office on Tuesday.
- The white car was a Renault and was parked outside the office on Monday.

94.

China

Iran

Yemen

Armenia

India

95.

The connecting word is SPORTS

Tennis

Basketball

Cricket

Baseball

Rugby

Golf

96.

The connection is FIRE

Lighter

Proof

Work

Wood

Fly

97.

Those who can imagine anything, can create the impossible.

98.

Each binary number represents the value of a letter in the alphabet, where A=1, B=2, etc

- GOLDFINGER
- MOONRAKER
- THUNDERBALL
- YOU ONLY LIVE TWICE
- LIVE AND LET DIE

99.

ORZO

GEMELLI

FETTUCCINE

FARFALLE

ORECCHIETTE

100.

PACEMAKER

TOURNIQUET

SYRINGE

DEFIBRILLATOR

FORCEPS

CATHETER

101.

- CLASS: UNDERCLASS and CLASSROOMS
- FIRE: SUREFIRE and FIREBRAND
- LET: TABLET and LETDOWN
- PARK: BALLPARK and PARKWAY
- LIGHT: MOONLIGHT and LIGHTHEARTED
- BODY: SOMEBODY and BODYWORK

102.

OLIVER TWIST
DAVID COPPERFIELD
BLEAK HOUSE
THE PICKWICK PAPERS
OUR MUTUAL FRIEND
THE BATTLE OF LIFE

103.

Beat around the bush
Cutting corners
Hit the sack
The last straw
Miss the boat

104.

The connection is HATS
- Bowler
- Busby: bus by
- Deerstalker: deer stalker
- Fez
- Sombrero: sombrer 'o'

105.

BAHT
DRACHMA
RAND
SHEKEL
GUILDER
REAL

106.

- Fighter was the first album to be released, and is 47 minutes long.
- Bronze Lows was the second album to be released, and is 65 minutes long.
- The Shadows Approach was the third album to be released, and is 58 minutes long.
- Sleep Well was the fourth album to be released, and is 78 minutes long.

107.

Picasso
Monet
Kahlo
Matisse
Vermeer

108.

The connecting word is WHEELS
Motorbike
Automobile
Bicycle
Scooter
Wheelbarrow
Rollerblades

109.

The connection is PALINDROME
Kayak
Noon
Level
Madam
Radar

110.

If a machine is expected to be infallible, it cannot also be intelligent.

111.
Each value is a code in the ASCII character set, so 32=space, 65=A, 66=B etc and then 97=a, 98=b etc
- VIRGINIA HALL
- SIDNEY REILLY
- JAMES ARMISTEAD
- MATA HARI
- GIACOMO CASANOVA

112.
BEYONCÉ
ELVIS PRESLEY
JUSTIN BIEBER
AXL ROSE
ANNIE LENNOX

113.
AMYGDALA
CEREBRAL CORTEX
HIPPOCAMPUS
FRONTAL LOBE
MEDULLA OBLONGATA
PITUITARY GLAND

114.
- FRAME: MAINFRAME and FRAMEWORK
- SCRIPT: TYPESCRIPT and SCRIPTWRITER
- HILL: ANTHILL and HILLSIDE
- CAP: SKULLCAP and CAPABILITY
- SEES: OVERSEES and SEESAWED
- COVER: HARDCOVER and COVERALL

115.
BLANCHE INGRAM
EDWARD ROCHESTER
ADELE VARENS
BERTHA MASON
GRACE POOLE
ELIZA REED

116.
On the ball
Pulling your leg
Raining cats and dogs
Barking up the wrong tree
Costs an arm and a leg

117.
The connection is FILM DIRECTORS
- Eastwood: east wood
- Hitchcock: hitch cock
- Nolan: no LAN
- Tarantino: tar ant in 'o'
- Bergman: berg man

118.
AMAZON RAINFOREST
KOMODO ISLAND
TABLE MOUNTAIN
HA LONG BAY
MOUNT KILIMANJARO

119.

- Crow has been undercover in London for a week.
- Eagle has been undercover in Amsterdam for six months.
- Falcon has been undercover in Paris for a month.
- Raven has been undercover in Berlin for a fortnight.

120.

Zeus

Athena

Hera

Ares

Poseidon

121.

The connecting word is INSECTS

Grasshopper

Ladybird

Cricket

Butterfly

Beetle

Bumblebee

Mantis

122.

The connection is 3 LETTERS IN ALPHABETICAL ORDER

Definite

Hijack

Rijksmuseum

Constantinople

Bratwurst

123.

We are not interested in the fact that the brain has the consistency of cold porridge.

124.

Each number represents the hexadecimal representation of the ASCII value of each character — see the solution to puzzle 111

- JOHN LE CARRE
- IAN FLEMING
- GRAHAM GREENE
- ROBERT LUDLUM
- KEN FOLLETT

125.

CASPIAN SEA

INDIAN OCEAN

ARABIAN SEA

AMAZON (RIVER)

AEGEAN SEA

126.

TOURMALINE

TURQUOISE

MALACHITE

LAPIS LAZULI

OBSIDIAN

CITRINE

127.

- TOE: TIPTOE and TOENAIL
- GRAPHIC: TYPOGRAPHIC and GRAPHICALLY
- KEY: DONKEY and KEYSTROKE
- VINE: GRAPEVINE and VINEYARD
- DRAW: WITHDRAW and DRAWBACK
- OUT: COOKOUT and OUTSMART

128.

- MESOPOTAMIA, *Murder in Mesopotamia*
- NILE, *Death on the Nile*
- BAGHDAD, *They Came to Baghdad*
- CARIBBEAN, *A Caribbean Mystery*
- FRANKFURT, *Passenger to Frankfurt*
- ORIENT, *Murder on the Orient Express*

129.

Hit the nail on the head

A piece of cake

Wild goose chase

Bigger fish to fry

Penny for your thoughts

130.

- Blue uses a Beretta and 6mm bullets.
- Orange uses a Walther and 4mm bullets.
- Pink uses a Glock and 2mm bullets.
- Red uses a Colt and 3mm bullets.
- So Pink killed Green.

131.

Togo

Mali

Angola

Rwanda

Comoros

132.

The connecting word is CARTOON

Mickey Mouse

Bugs Bunny

Popeye

Donald Duck

Tweety

Tom Cat

Spongebob

133.

The connection is that they are all WORDS WHICH ARE BOTH NOUNS AND VERBS

Present

Permit

Contest

Whistle

Insult

134.

Science is a differential equation. Religion is a boundary condition

135.

The rail fence encryption uses three rails.
Draw out a table with three rows and as many
column as there are letters, then write the
given text in a bouncing diagonal line across
the table, starting at the top left. You can then
read the solution off the rows.

- I WAS RUNNING AWAY — *The Spy Who Loved Me*
- THE SCENT AND SMOKE AND SWEAT OF A CASINO ARE NAUSEATING AT THREE IN THE MORNING — *Casino Royale*
- THE EYES BEHIND THE WIDE BLACK RUBBER GOGGLES WERE COLD AS FLINT — *For Your Eyes Only*
- THERE ARE MOMENTS OF GREAT LUXURY IN THE LIFE OF A SECRET AGENT — *Live and Let Die*
- THE TWO THIRTY-EIGHTS ROARED SIMULTANEOUSLY — *Moonraker*

136.

EISENHOWER
KENNEDY
HAYES
PIERCE
JEFFERSON

137.

ACCORDION
BAGPIPES
CONCERTINA
GLOCKENSPIEL
DIDGERIDOO
SAXOPHONE

NOTES